ROCKS AND MINERALS

BY RICHARD FORTEY

Cathay Books

CONTENTS

Left The Giant's Causeway, Co. Antrim, Northern Ireland. Both the cliffs and the distinctive stone columns in the foreground are formed naturally from the rock basalt.

INTRODUCTION

No matter where we live there is rock beneath us. The rocks forming the earth's crust form the platform on which the events of the living world are acted out. Yet the rocks themselves have been the subject of intense scientific scrutiny for only the last century and a half, and we are just beginning to penetrate the secrets of the earth's deep interior. As with all other fields of scientific investigation, the more rocks are studied the more complex they are seen to be, the more different kinds are distinguished, and the more names are applied to their description. This book shows some of the more common or important types of rock, a number of economically important minerals, and some of the gemstones that attracted people's attention long before they began to understand the processes of their formation.

All rocks are composed of minerals. Every mineral has a specific chemical composition, and the atoms that compose it are arranged in an equally characteristic way. There are a large but finite number of different minerals because atoms can only join together and arrange themselves in a limited number of ways. Minerals vary widely in their abundance, partly depending on the abundance of the elements that compose their atomic structure. The mineral calcite, for example, is generally widespread, being composed of the common elements carbon, calcium and oxygen. Other mineral species are so rare that they are known from literally two or three crystals.

A rock may be composed of only one mineral, or of several different minerals in various combinations. The rock limestone is usually composed entirely of the mineral calcite. But granite is composed of the minerals felspar, quartz and mica, with other minor components. The name given to a rock depends on the combination of minerals it displays, and the natural mode of origin of the rock itself.

Not surprisingly, there are many hundreds of different rock types. The size of the mineral grains composing the rock can vary enormously. In rocks such as granite the individual mineral grains can be observed easily with the naked eye. In clays (which are, geologically speaking, as much rocks as granite) the individual mineral crystals are so small that they can only be seen with an electron microscope.

When rocks are exposed at the surface, the action of the weather over long periods of time often alters the component minerals, so to identify a rock accurately fresh specimens should be collected. In rocks exploited commercially, the valuable mineral can often form only a small proportion of the rock, and the weathering process can play a vital part in concentrating the valuable ore.

Rocks can be divided into three major groups according to their mode of formation. Perhaps the greatest areas on the continents are covered by *sedimentary* rocks. These are rocks that were originally deposited as soft sediments on the bottom of the sea, or on the beds of lakes or rivers, or as sands and other deposits formed in deserts. The sediments themselves are derived from the breakdown of older rocks by the processes of weathering.

Areas now dry land were once covered by the oceans in which the sediments were deposited. The history of sedimentary rocks extends backwards in time for several thousands of millions of years, and during this immense stretch of time the areas that are now dry land were inundated by the sea on numerous occasions. There have been several periods when almost all Europe and North America were drowned beneath the sea. The legacy of such events is the covering of sedimentary rocks over large areas of these continents. Time changes initially soft sediments into harder rocks, but not all need a hammer to split them.

Amethyst (*right*) is a very popular quartz crystal, with a colouring between purple and violet.

4

Sedimentary rocks are found on land today because the land areas have risen (and the sea may be at a lower level then than at some periods). Of course, sediments continue to accumulate today on the sea floors around the coasts, and on deltas and in lakes. These will in their turn become the sedimentary rocks of the next millennia; limestones, sandstones, shales and clays are familiar examples. Such rocks may entomb the remains of extinct animal or plant life – fossils.

The second group of rocks are those of *igneous* origin. We can see igneous rocks forming today when volcanoes erupt and great masses of lava pour out of fissures or craters to solidify in massive flows of basalt. Sometimes volcanoes blow up completely to form hot flows of incandescent ash and rock fragments. These igneous rocks originated from deep in the earth as liquid rock or magma.

Although we can observe the formation of volcanic rocks, there are other kinds of igneous rocks which are formed at great depth within the earth's hot centre, and hence cannot be seen in the making. These rocks usually have larger crystals than is the case with volcanic rocks, because they cooled more slowly. Naturally, they will never contain any traces of former animal life. The commonest of these 'deep-seated' igneous rocks is granite and its relatives. Tongues of liquid rock from a granite mass may invade the surrounding rocks to give rise to hard rock forms called *dykes* and *sills*. Because great tracts of granite shoulder their way into the surrounding rocks, baking them, and incorporating lumps into its mass, granite bodies are often referred to as *intrusions*. For a granite to be

exposed at the surface, as on Dartmoor, England, millions of years of erosion are required to strip away the overlying rocks. Deep granite rocks may lie buried beneath covers of sedimentary rocks, awaiting their turn to be uncovered by erosion. The third major class is the *metamorphic* rocks. 'Metamorphic' means 'changed form', and that is exactly what they are: rocks which started as either sedimentary or igneous, and which have drastically changed their appearance as a result of pressure, heat or a combination of the two. The pressure often results in a banding of the minerals in metamorphic rocks (foliation), and the conditions forming them produce peculiar minerals that are found in neither of the other two classes. Metamorphic rocks are formed particularly deep beneath mountain belts such as the Himalayas, where the rocks of the earth's crust are being squeezed between the Indian and Asian blocks, resulting in both their elevation at the surface, and their being forced downwards into the hot interior of the earth. The most abundant metamorphic rocks are slates, schists and gneisses, while the most familiar is probably marble, which is metamorphosed limestone.

Minerals are identified from their chemical composition and their atomic structure, but neither of these can be evaluated immediately by the amateur at home. Fortunately there are other characteristics. The shape of the crystal is important, for it is related to the way the atoms are arranged. Some minerals (galena, rock salt and fluorspar are examples) occur in cubes, or modifications of cubes such as eight-sided crystals, with the same atomic structure. Other crystals occur in lengthened crystals or in radiating masses of fine needles. Some lengthened crystals are four-sided (for example, zircon), others often six-sided (quartz and beryl). Prismatic crystals may be capped by pyramidal crystal faces.

Some crystals can become very complex indeed, with dozens of faces on a single natural crystal. It must be emphasized that the cut faces on gemstones are applied by the jeweller, and have nothing to do with the crystal faces of the naturally occurring mineral. Many minerals can display more than one crystal form, depending on how the different faces 'grow' while the crystal is forming. Other minerals characteristically occur in masses in which single crystals cannot be seen. Colour is an important way of recognizing minerals, and is vital for distinguishing gemstones from those of lesser quality. Many have particularly distinctive colours – such as the deep blue lapis lazuli shown on page 54. Other minerals can vary in colour according to tiny traces of chemical impurities. Beryl, for example, can be colourless, but its several gem varieties carry different names according to colour: emerald (green), aquamarine (blue) and morganite (pink).

Minerals vary widely in their hardness: some, such as talc, are soft enough to be scratched with a finger nail, while diamonds are harder than anything else in nature. Hardness is an easy test for distinguishing common colourless minerals. Quartz is too hard to be scratched by a penknife, while calcite, which can look similar at first glance, is easily scratched with a knife.

Many minerals have a characteristic way of breaking – natural lines of weakness run through the crystals, again related to atomic structure. This break-line, or cleavage, can provide a quick way of distinguishing dark mica (biotite) from other, similarly coloured minerals, because mica

can be 'flaked' with a penknife into almost infinitely thin, shiny sheets. Fluorite has a typical way of breaking into eight-sided crystals along its cleavage planes.

A few minerals are so conspicuously dense that their exceptional weight can easily distinguish them from other specimens in the hand. The barium mineral barytes is a rather ordinary looking white mineral which might be confused with quartz, but its heavier weight betrays its identity.

Scientific study of rocks is often pursued by cutting slices through the rock so thin that they are transparent, and can then be examined under the microscope. Identification of component minerals is easier this way.

Any area will have its own interesting rocks to examine. With a little experience, good sites for mineral specimens can be discovered, particularly where there are igneous or metamorphic rocks in the vicinity. Different rock types are marked on geological maps, which can be used as a guide to likely mineral sites. Old mine workings will almost always yield interesting mineral specimens. The amateur may even be lucky enough to discover a specimen of gem quality.

Haematite (*left*) is iron oxide; its remarkable colouring comes through the refraction of light in the mineral's surface layer. Photomicrographs reveal the intricate structure of rocks; (*below*) Olivine basalt comes under the magnifying lens.

COMMON ROCKS

Wherever we live the rocks beneath us play an important part in shaping the land-forms. Hard rocks, soft rocks, porous rocks and layered rocks all have characteristic landscapes associated with them. The Devil's Chimney (*left*), Leckhampton, England, has been formed in a quarry cut into a sedimentary rock known as Oolite.

Sedimentary Rocks

Two of the commonest types of sedimentary rocks are limestone and sandstone. Limestone is composed of the mineral calcite. Many limestones are made from the fossil shells of animals with calcite skeletons, and thick limestone formations may extend over hundreds of square miles. Many of the limestones forming today are in warm water regions, and the same seems to have applied in the past.

The limestone pavement above Malham Cove, Yorkshire, England (*right*) consists of great blocks of limestone criss-crossed with deep fissures which are known as clints and grykes. They were formed by the weathering action of rainwater which becomes slightly acid when carbon dioxide or sulphurous gases in the air are dissolved in it. Limestone effervesces and dissolves in weak acids. Malham Cove is an enormous semi-circular limestone cliff; at one time a waterfall higher than Niagara poured over it.

Sandstone (*below*) is composed of thousands of small grains of the mineral quartz. This sort of rock can originate as a fossil beach sand, or can be the record of a past desert climate. Some fossil sandstones preserve the ripple marks made by the sea that once washed over them.

Coal

The familiarity of coal should not blind us to its value. Coal is largely composed of the element carbon, but many other useful by-products are also obtainable from it. Coal was produced from the fossil remains of generations of trees. Most of the coal used in Europe and North America originated from trees that flourished in the lush tropical swamps of the Carboniferous period. Sometimes the fossils of the leaves or roots of the trees can be found in association with the coal.

(*Left*) mechanized coal-mining in progress: a chainless-haulage coal-cutting shearer in operation at Daw Hill Colliery, near Coventry, England. It takes about sixteen units of plant matter to make one unit of coal. Peat and lignite, also used as fuel in some parts of the world, are formed in similar conditions. Lignite is a soft brown coal, which has not gone so far along the process of decomposition.

Often coal is found in seams near the surface of the earth (*below*). In other places it may be extracted by excavating huge open-cast mines, where the surface soil is stripped away, together with any other rocks overlying the coal itself. But when, as is most normal, coal is buried at great depths, it must be mined. Shafts are dug downwards into the earth until they reach the mineral seams. Then horizontal shafts are constructed to follow the seam of coal, often extending for miles underground.

Marble

Marble is produced by the action of heat and pressure on limestone. If the limestone is remarkably pure, a pure white marble results. Original impurities can produce a variety of metamorphic minerals which give the distinctive mottling and veining that has made marble such a popular ornamental stone.

Marble quarrying is seen in progress at Carrara, Italy (*left*), the source of some of the world's best-known deposits of white marble. This has a white, sugary appearance, and is made up of a patterning of interlocked calcite minerals. Pure limestone sedimentary rocks and shelly limestones were metamorphosed in its formation. Marble has long been used for ornamentation and sculpture. For example, the ancient Greeks made skilled and widespread use of this material. Their main quarries were at Paros and at Mount Pentelikon, near Athens. Italy took over as a prime source for marble in the middle ages. It was frequently used during this period for the decoration of churches and for sculpture.

One popular marble of this period was the 'marble of the ruins' from Florence.

Other sources of white marble include Ruszikaer in Hungary, Peak in Malaya, and parts of the Austrian Tyrol. Multi-coloured marbles are much more common. They originate from limestones which originally contained impurities. World-famous examples include the light green marble found in Connemara, Ireland. Black marble is found in Kilkenny, Ireland; Namur, Belgium; and Mayenne, France. Various other colours of marble are found in other areas, including Barstow, Crestmore and Twin Lakes, California, USA. Today marble is often quarried by the use of explosives, which dislodge it and break it up. However slabs are also obtained by sawing and wedging the rock, which avoids causing the development of tiny cracks which damage it. Top left is an example of brown marble. Purbeck limestones (*top right*) are named after the Isle of Purbeck, southern England, where they are found. They are rich in the shells of freshwater snails since they were formed in the bed of an early lake. Purbeck limestones take a good polish and hence are often known as marbles. They are widely used for building and in the interior decoration of churches.

VALUABLE MINERALS

From earliest times some rare minerals have been prized for their value and beauty. Such metals as gold and silver have been constant symbols of riches and power. On the left is some native silver in its fibrous form.

Silver and Gold

Silver is one of the few elements that occur pure – native – as an ore. Although silver can occur in cubic crystals, it usually occurs in rather irregular masses, or sometimes as fibrous threads (*previous page*). Most of the silver used today is derived from other ores. But native silver has been used for a long time in the manufacture of ornaments and coins. Silver does not survive the ravages of time as well as gold, however. Native silver may occur along with other native metals, gold and copper, or with other sulphide minerals. Famous occurrences were the mines at Kongsberg in Norway, which were productive for several centuries, and the old mines in Saxony. Some huge nuggets of native silver have been recovered from the copper mines in Cobalt, Ontario.

Gold has been called a 'noble metal' because of its reluctance to combine with any other elements. The same quality means that it occurs in the rocks as native, pure gold. The element is quite widely distributed in small amounts. Most

of the commercially mined gold is recovered from rocks in which the gold forms only a small percentage of the whole. Great weights of rock have to be processed to recover even a very small weight of gold. In the past, much more concentrated occurrences of gold in mineral veins could be processed by hand, and large nuggets were frequent. These discoveries produced the gold rushes of the nineteenth century. There is a little gold in Britain in the Welsh hills which is still exploited in a desultory way. The largest supply of the world's gold comes from Witwatersrand, Johannesburg, South Africa.

The native gold nugget (*centre*) was found in Australia. Native gold is sometimes found embedded in other minerals, such as calcite (*far left*). Because of its rarity and value, gold is often used to make religious or ceremonial objects. The gold ceremonial vessel in the shape of a dove (*below*) comes from the twelfth or thirteenth-century civilization of Peru.
Gold may have been the first metal that men encountered. It may have been discovered in the gravels and streambeds; man then devoted much energy to finding more of the alluring metal. Gold decorative objects from as far back as the Early Stone Age have been found.

Platinum

At present much of the world's platinum (*below*) comes from the Soviet Union, Canada and South Africa. Platinum is even more resistant to chemical attack than gold, and this has led to its use in the manufacture of chemical apparatus that has to resist acids and high temperatures. The same qualities make platinum a durable material for jewellery (*right*). The even rarer elements iridium and palladium occur associated with platinum.

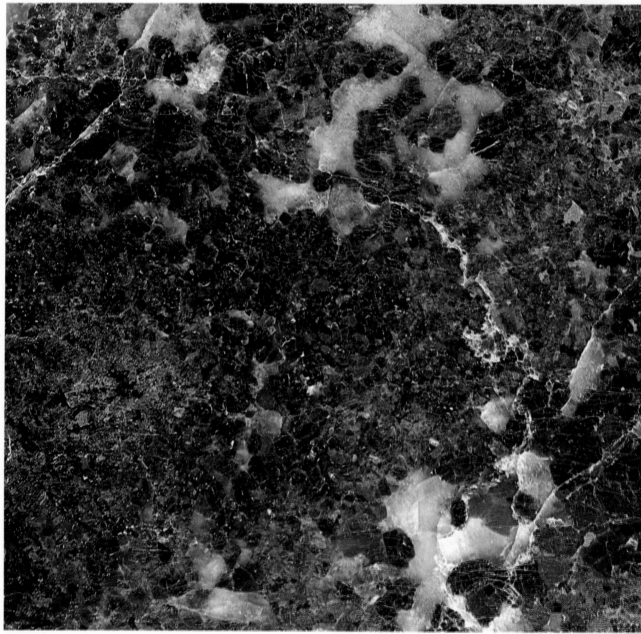

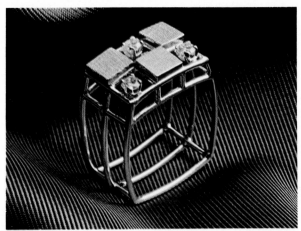

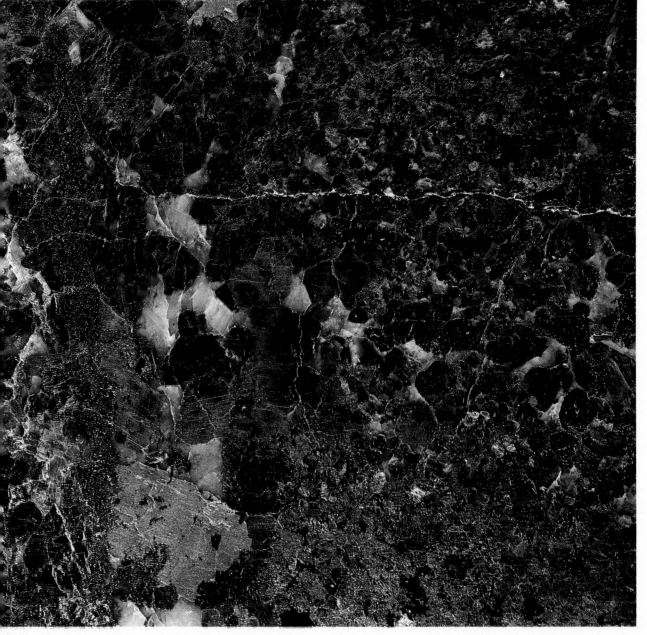

Sulphur and Copper

Two other elements that occur native are copper (*below*) and sulphur (*left*). Like silver and gold, copper can occur in twisted irregular masses, sometimes of great weight. Copper was probably the first metal used to make utensils and weapons. Native copper is only a minor source of the metal today; most is derived from copper sulphides.

Sulphur can occur in well-formed crystals or as incrustations with a characteristic yellow colour. Sulphurous springs are associated with volcanoes, and sulphur itself is deposited around fumaroles (vents from which volcanic gases escape). This was one of its earliest sources for alchemical preparations and gunpowder. A lot of the sulphur used today occurs in sedimentary rocks and it has numerous industrial uses.

A large amount of sulphur is deposited from hot springs such as the Mammoth Hot Springs at Yellowstone Park, Wyoming, USA (*far left*). Hot springs are believed to represent the last stages of volcanic activity.

Iron and Lead

Magnetite (*top left*), an oxide of iron and an important iron ore, is, as its name suggests, strongly magnetic. In the form of *lodestones* magnetite was the first kind of natural magnet to be discovered. It has a characteristic black colour, and often occurs in eight-sided (octahedral) crystals.

Pyrite (*top right*), or iron pyrites, is a sulphide of iron. It is one of the commonest of the iron minerals, widely distributed in rocks of all kinds. When it occurs well-formed, it is usually in cubic crystals, the faces of the cube being scored or striated. It often occurs in slightly metamorphosed shales. The characteristic brassy yellow colour has led to its confusion with gold – hence its common name 'fool's gold'. It is also one of the most frequent minerals in veins associated with igneous rocks. It is no longer an important ore of iron, compared with haematite and magnetite.

Galena (*bottom left*) is the important ore of lead (lead sulphide), often with traces of silver. As might be expected, galena is noticeably heavy, and has a typical lead-grey appearance. It nearly always occurs as cubic crystals. It is quite a common ore of mineral veins derived from igneous rocks. It is found in the valleys of the Missouri and Mississippi in the USA, and in several central European states.

From ancient times lead was obtained from galena. The Babylonians used it for making lead vases and the Romans to construct water pipes. With the invention of printing, lead became adopted as the basic metal for type. Compounds of lead are often used for making paints and enamels.

The Italian Dolomites (*right*) are rich in several important minerals, as well as being renowned for their great natural beauty.

Uranium

Pitchblende (*bottom left*) is the most abundant ore of uranium, of which it is the oxide. When well-crystallized, pitchblende is known as uranite. It is not a common mineral, and is extremely valuable as a chief source of radioactive elements. Uranium is one of the heaviest elements, so pitchblende is unusually dense. It is also the source of one of the rarest of elements – radium – first isolated by Marie Curie. It would be unusual to obtain more than one gram of radium from 500 tons of ore. Radium has become important in the treatment of cancer by radioactivity. The inert gas helium, produced by the radioactive breakdown of uranium, was also first discovered in pitchblende. A complex refining process is necessary to produce uranium (*bottom right*), which is carefully packed in small pellets for use as fuel in nuclear reactors (*top left*).

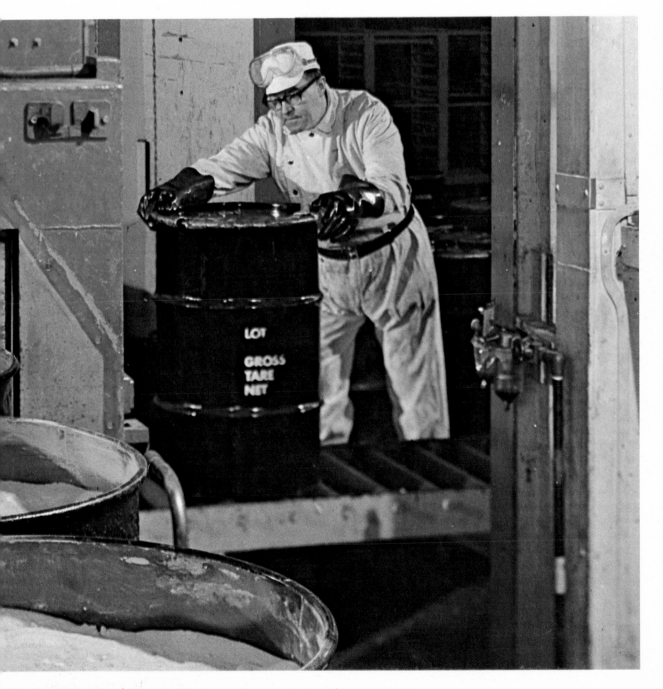

Asbestos

Mineral asbestos has a distinctive fibrous texture. It is heat resistant and frequently used in construction work to ensure fire protection. It can be woven into fabric, and then made up into protective garments for such workers as firemen. Asbestos is found in thick enough deposits to be mined in Canada, where major excavations are undertaken to extract asbestos ore. After it has been refined, the asbestos is made up into sheets.

Asbestos belongs to the amphibole family, which includes the silicates of magnesium, iron, calcium, sodium and potassium. Hornblende, a complex mineral which contains sodium, calcium, magnesium, iron, aluminium, silica, oxygen and hydrogen, is a common member of this family. The asbestos pictured (*below*) is Hornblende asbestos from the Austrian Tyrol (*right*). It is a particularly clear example of a fibrous mineral, consisting of very compact bundles of long, fibrous, almost silky crystals. They can normally be easily stripped off in small groups from the fibrous mass.

Other members of the amphibole group bear little resemblance to asbestos; they include nephrite, a form of jade. This is among the toughest minerals and is often used for ornamentation, especially in China.

MINERAL WEALTH OF THE WORLD

Almost everything that we now regard as commonplace essentials in our lives – even the food we eat – depends on the mineral wealth of the earth. Our agriculture needs fertilizers, our electricity needs copper conductors, and our machines and utensils are inconceivable without iron or aluminium. All the raw materials start as minerals beneath the ground. Human material progress ran parallel to the discovery of techniques for the extraction of metals from their ores. Iron-smelting conferred advantages on its discoverers that displaced the users of bronze. The exploitation of the earth's mineral resources continues today on an unprecedented scale.

It is fortunate that the mineral wealth of the earth is not distributed at random over the surface of the globe. Elements that are rare in nature are concentrated locally into rich seams of minerals. When these are rich enough for commercial exploitation the mineral deposits are called *ores*. Improved extraction techniques mean that a wider range of deposits is used as ore today than in the last century.

Mining companies employ geologists to seek out new ore deposits, and when they are discovered claims are still 'staked'. But the days of the lone prospector – that bewhiskered character sustained through years of hardship by the belief that one day he would 'strike it rich' – are almost over. Many valuable deposits today are found at depth, and are only detectable by modern instruments.

Many valuable minerals are found in veins associated with igneous rocks. The ores of zinc, silver, tin and lead are found in this form. The minerals are deposited in the veins from solutions saturated with gases that have been 'boiled off' the hot igneous rocks. These solutions escape into the surrounding rocks, often penetrating along cracks, faults or joints for considerable distances. Once a rich vein is

discovered it may then be worked along its length until it peters out, or becomes too deep and dangerous to work.

Worthless minerals, particularly vein quartz, usually accompany the valuable ore, and these are left in spoil heaps which disfigure many a mining landscape. The spoil heaps may be fruitful hunting grounds for the amateur mineral collector, however. Where igneous rocks have cooled very slowly in the presence of gases, very large crystals may result. In the rock known as pegmatite large, chemically-pure crystals of quartz, beryl, tourmaline and felspar are found. They have many commercial uses, including jewellery.

Few metals occur *native* (pure), and not combined with any other element. Gold is one of the few, but rarely occurs in large nuggets that can make a fortune at a stroke. Most of the 'gold' that people discover in pebbles on the beach is worthless iron pyrites, 'fool's gold'. Because of its purity and ease of working, gold was one of the first metals to be used by man. Egyptian and Inca gold has survived for hundreds of years untarnished.

Gold

Most gold extracted today occurs scattered, or disseminated, in very low concentrations in the host rock from which it is extracted by chemical processes. When such rocks are eroded by rivers, the heavy gold is often concentrated into sands on the stream bed. It is this sort of river sand that is 'panned' for gold by the prospector. The heavy gold particles are collected in the bottom of the pan, while the lighter sand and mud is washed away. Such river sediments can form commercial ores, when they are known as placer deposits. Copper and silver can also occur native, and may also be found as nuggets, as well as in various ores.

Iron

For sheer bulk, iron is probably the most widely-exploited element. Many iron ores are of sedimentary origin. Unlike rarer metals, iron ores are often worked in great open pits (open cast mining), because the constant demand for iron makes large scale working necessary. Iron Age man tended to exploit smaller, easily accessible sources. They cut down trees to supply charcoal for smelting, and were responsible for the destruction of some of the primeval forests. Fortunately iron is one of nature's commonest elements, and can be found in commercial quantities in igneous and metamorphic rocks, as well as sediments. We are unlikely to run out of iron and steel in the future.

Phosphate minerals

These are vital in the manufacture of fertilizers, and are also found in appreciable quantities in sedimentary rocks. These sources are now replacing the more traditional ones – notably the excreta of seabirds that produced highly concentrated guano, which was gathered from the mounds accumulating on offshore islands near the birds' feeding grounds.

Rock Salt

Other important deposits had their origins in seas that vanished long ago. These are crystals laid down when former seas evaporated in arid tropical climates. Something of the same process is happening today in the Dead Sea, which is becoming more and more saline. When enough water has evaporated, crystals start to be thrown out of solution. Much of this material is rock salt, but it is accompanied by other minerals, such as gypsum and various salts of potash, with a wide variety of uses – everything from fertilizers to plastics and building materials. Many of these deposits are now found at great depths, and mining is carried on underground. Even the Mediterranean Sea is known to have 'dried out' at one stage in its long history.

Coal

Some substances with a particular chemical composition can exist in several different mineral forms (polymorphs). Coal, the fossilized and chemically transformed remains of extinct trees, is composed of the element carbon, as is charcoal. When the coal is heated at depth in the earth's crust, it becomes hardened into valuable anthracite. With further heat and pressure, the carbon is transformed into the mineral graphite (formerly used as 'lead' in pencils). Graphite is soft and slippery, because its atoms are arranged in sheets that can slide over one another, a property that leads to its use in lubricants.

Diamond

But when carbon is subjected to the enormous pressures and high temperatures of very deep levels beneath the earth's surface, the atoms are rearranged again to take up as little room as possible. This results in a very hard substance; the black colour of the familiar carbon is quite lost, and the result is diamond. Because the conditions needed to produce diamonds are so unusual, it is not surprising that they are rare. The diamonds of South Africa occur in 'diamond pipes', deep holes through the earth's crust that have allowed minerals formed at huge depths beneath the earth to reach the surface. It took many years to simulate the natural conditions and produce artificial diamonds on a commercial scale, and nature still holds the secret of producing the flawless gemstones that have been used as a measure of wealth for hundreds of years, although only about 23 per cent of those found are suitable as gems.

PRECIOUS STONES

Precious stones were first used by man in prehistoric times. The most ancient reports of their use come from India and the east Mediterranean region. Quartz appears in a great variety of crystal forms; on the left it is with chalcopyrite (copper ore) crystals.

Diamond

Diamonds remain the most sought after of precious stones (*left*). Their hardness is such that cutting diamonds is a very skilled operation. The largest diamond ever found was the Cullinan Diamond, weighing 3106 carats, and subsequently cut into nine large stones and 96 smaller brilliants.

Zircon

Zircon, the silicate of the rare element zirconium, is a frequent additional mineral in granites and other igneous rocks. It is a hard and resistant mineral that may be concentrated in sands derived from the weathering of granites. Gem-quality zircons have a wide range of colours, from colourless to red or brown. Cut zircon stones have many of the qualities of diamond.

Beryl

Beryl (*top right*) is a silicate compound of aluminium and the rare element beryllium. Its most common occurrence is in coarse-grained rocks associated with granites, where crystals can achieve considerable sizes. Of the various colours that beryl may be – gold, blue, pink, or green – it is the green variety, emerald, that is the most sought after (*top left, right*). Colombia in South America has been the principal source of gem emeralds for a long time. Well-formed emeralds are even more valuable than diamonds. Aquamarine and rose beryl are more common varieties. The usual natural forms of all beryls are long, six-sided crystals. The non-gem varieties are used as a source of the light metal, beryllium.

Exceptional examples of aquamarine have been found in Brazil, Siberia and the Urals. In south Brazil, large gem-quality aquamarines of a magnificent pale blue have been found frequently. The largest ground aquamarine is in the Smithsonian Institution, Washington,

D.C., in the USA; it too originated in Brazil. Queen Cleopatra is traditionally believed to have had her portrait engraved in emerald. Certainly emerald mines were worked in Egypt during her reign, and much earlier. The ancient Romans, the Arabs and the Turks all in turn went to Egypt in search of emeralds.

Emeralds were valued in other parts of the world too. The Peruvians are supposed to have worshipped an emerald the size of an ostrich egg. Before the Spanish went to South America, the Indians were mining emeralds in Colombia. Emeralds were prized in Asia too. In the Buddhist temple at Kandy, Sri Lanka, there is a little statue of the Buddha, carved from a single emerald. The most acclaimed deposits of emerald were south of Koseir, Egypt, but these mines are now disused. Today the best emerald specimens are found near Musso, Colombia. Other sources of this much-sought stone include the Urals, USSR, and the Transvaal of South Africa.

The characteristic green colour of the emerald is caused by chromium impurities present in the crystal. Emeralds are normally mined where the rock in which they are formed has been exposed to the air by weathering processes.

Tourmaline and Topaz

Tourmaline (*below and right*) usually grows in long crystals with scored faces. It is highly variable, often black, but red, pink, green, blue and yellow varieties are known. Sometimes different-coloured varieties may grow concentrically. Tourmaline is quite an abundant mineral. Topaz (*far right*) occurs in long crystals in rather similar geological sites to beryl. It also can exhibit many different colours such as pale yellow, brown and pale blue.

Garnet

Garnet includes a wide variety of related minerals, most of which are characteristic of metamorphic rocks. Garnets are common in schists and gneisses, usually being of the red almandite variety, but most of these occurrences are of no commercial value. Well-formed garnet crystals may have twelve or more facets. Gem garnets are mostly of a beautiful claret-wine red colour (*right*). Garnet is one of the more common gemstones, but also one of the most attractive. (*Below and bottom*) Spessartine garnet: flakes of muscovite and reddish spessartine garnet embedded in felspar.

Corundum

The mineral corundum is the oxide of aluminium, and is common in metamorphic rocks. It usually occurs in crystals that tend to become barrel-shaped when weathered. The gem corundums include the deep red ruby, and the blue sapphire. Rubies are fairly immune to erosion, so when rocks containing rubies are weathered away, the valuable gems are ultimately concentrated. Famous areas for rubies and sapphires are in Burma, Thailand and Sri Lanka; in the latter the precious stones occur in stream gravels. Synthetic rubies and sapphires are now manufactured with considerable success. Corundum is a very hard mineral, second only to the diamond.

Chrysoberyl
and Rock Crystal

Chrysoberyl is an uncommon mineral, and, like beryl, contains the rare element beryllium. It is hard and resistant, and survives the weathering of its host rock to be concentrated into river sands and gravels. There are several gem varieties (*below*), the commonest of which is yellow-green. Alexandrite is a magnificent emerald green, but appears red in artificial light. Cat's eye has a remarkable ability to reflect a long, narrow beam of light which changes its position as the stone is moved.

Quartz, by contrast, is one of the commonest of minerals (*right*). The totally clear variety, rock crystal (*bottom right*), is an attractive gemstone, and is abundant enough to be relatively inexpensive.

Rock crystal is normally found in sedimentary rocks such as limestones. It often occurs in veins together with adularia, chlorite and titanic minerals. All of these are greatly valued. Some of the oldest and best-known rock-crystal deposits are in the Swiss Alps (*right*) where stones are sold to tourists at a high price. But the more highly-prized examples of crystals of rock crystal are found in cavities in the renowned snow-white marble from Carrara in northern Italy. Their distinctive transparency and lustre are strongly reminiscent of diamonds. Rock crystal received its name because it resembles ice (the Greek word 'crystal' means ice).

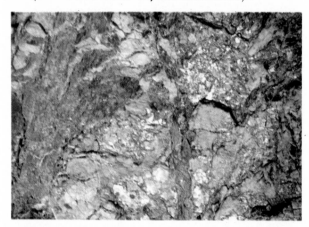

Opal and Felspar

Felspar (or feldspar) is a most abundant mineral, found in igneous and metamorphic rocks. Most of the felspars are of no interest as semi-precious stones. A green variety, amazonstone, is used as an ornamental stone. Moonstone is a variety which shows a play of colours resembling that of opal. The variety known as labradorite (*top left*) is used as ornamental facing stone.

Labradorite was first discovered two hundred years ago by a missionary named Father Adolf, on the east shore of the Labrador peninsula, Canada (hence its name). The crystals appeared to be dull grey, but when they were turned, they changed to an attractive dark blue and green colouring. Large deposits were later discovered in the Ukraine, and were used for small ornaments and jewels. The deposits on the Labrador coast remain the world's most important source. Finland also has major labradorite deposits.

Albite (*top centre*) is a white variety of felspar, with small, short crystals. It is found naturally as a crystal in fissures in a variety of rocks. It is especially common in the Austrian Tyrol; Polish Silesia; Moravia; Cornwall, England, and the Mountains of Mourne, Northern Ireland.

Opal (*top right*) is the rarest form of silica, the usual form being quartz. The gem varieties are recognized by their characteristic iridescence, which is produced by the mineral splitting ordinary light into its component colours. Opal is often deposited from hot springs, or from hot, mineral-bearing water passing through the rocks. Precious opal is valuable, and forms the basis of an extensive mining industry in Australia. Opal is never found in crystalline form.

Precious opal (*right*) with its radiant beauty is the most sought-after variety. It is outstanding for the brilliant, iridescent play of its colours. Even more valuable is the black opal (*far right*). It is a darker variation of previous opal, and has an intensive colour change. It was discovered in Australia at the close of the nineteenth century, and was once prized as much as the diamond.

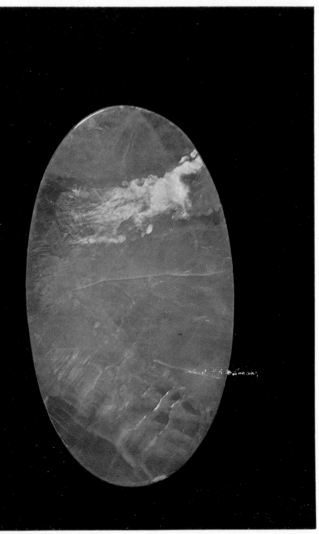

ORNAMENTAL STONES

Stones are valued for their ornamental use in building or for making decorative objects. As new styles and tastes replace the old, demand for one stone often replaces demand for another. But often the colour and texture of particularly beautiful stones bring them back into fashion. Jade has been used for ornaments for hundreds of years and is still a very popular material with many applications.

Chalcedony

Chalcedony (*below and right*) is another form of the versatile silica. The name is applied to the banded varieties of quartz, which have no visible crystals. The bands may be white or colourless. Very often they are coloured red, green or brown, and the coloured bands may alternate in a striking fashion. Chalcedony is not an uncommon form of quartz, and occurs in

large slabs, so it can be made into a variety of ornaments. Chalcedony is often deposited from solutions, and may be found lining fissures or cavities in rocks. Like all forms of quartz, chalcedony is resistant to erosion, and pebbles of the mineral are quite often found on beaches or in river gravel. These make attractive ornaments when split and polished.

The name jade is applied to several different minerals, all very hard, and with a characteristic milky-white to green colour (*previous page*). The working of jade has an extremely long history, especially in the East, where jade was used for weapons as well as ornaments. Varieties of jade occur particularly in metamorphic rocks. Jade minerals do not normally occur in single crystals, generally being found in massive or fibrous groupings which are more suitable for carving.

Blue Stones

The beautiful deep blue of lapis lazuli is highly characteristic. The mineral usually occurs in a massive form, without well-formed crystal faces. Lapis lazuli (*below*, with turquoise) is always found associated with iron pyrites, which gives the polished surfaces a mottled appearance. In its powdered form it was the source of the pigment ultramarine, used by artists. It is rather an uncommon material and occurs in metamorphosed limestones. A famous locality is in Afghanistan. As well as for making ornaments, lapis lazuli is used in complex Persian inlay work. The name means 'azure stone'.

The first known deposits of lapis lazuli were in Asia and Chile. The explorer Marco Polo reported seeing deposits of it in the upper reaches of the River Oxus, Afghanistan. It was probably from this area that the ancient Egyptians had previously taken lapis lazuli to make sacred amulets in the form of the scarab beetle.

Some precious stones are used in inlay work in furniture. (*Right*) a pietra-dura panel formed in lapis lazuli, agate cornelian and marble.

Turquoise (*below*, with lapis lazuli) was a particularly popular stone with the Turks at the time of the Ottoman Empire. There were turquoise mines in the Sinai Peninsula, which the ancient Egyptians once worked. The Turks bought the stone and transported it to Persia. Turquoise occurs in cracks in schists and sandstones, and occasionally in pegmatites. Today the major turquoise deposits are found near Nishapur, Iran; in Kazakhstan, USSR; in New Mexico, Utah and California, USA; and in Silesia, Poland. When it has particularly attractive and delicate colouring, turquoise is prized as a precious stone. Imitation turquoise is sometimes to be found; occasionally fossil bones are tinted blue in imitation. Collectors value rich blue turquoise most highly; but this is comparatively rare. It usually occurs stained brown from iron impurities.

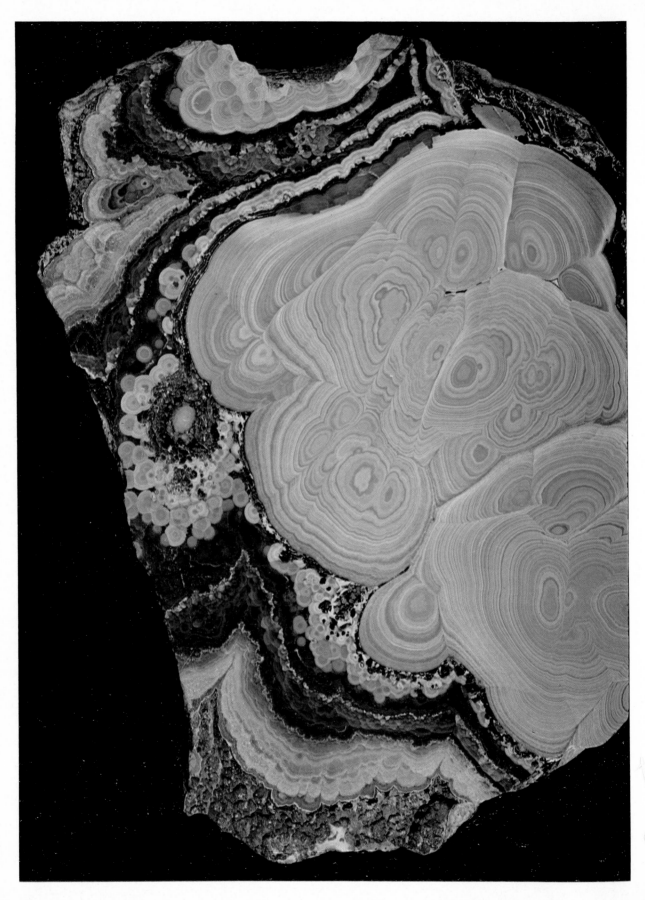

Malachite

Malachite is a carbonate of copper (*left and above*), with a distinctive, bright green colour. It usually occurs in masses of fibres forming rounded cushions, sheets or pillars. It is one of the most beautiful of the commoner minerals, often occurring in mineral veins with other ores of copper. It is usually associated with another, brightly coloured copper carbonate, deep blue azurite. The main use of malachite is as an ore of copper, but polished, it is also an attractive ornament. It has been most widely used in inlay work. A famous source of fine ornamental malachite is deep in the Ural Mountains of Russia.

Malachite is also found in Zaïre; in Cornwall, England; Tsumeb, Namibia; Burra, Australia; and Arizona, Utah and Nevada, in the USA. Most recently malachite has been discovered in Eilat in southern Israel.

The Greeks and Romans used malachite to make amulets to protect themselves and in particular their children from bad luck.

NON-MINERAL GEMSTONES

Several gems, such as pearls and amber, are not minerals. They have an organic origin, but a survey of some of the world's most popular stones would be incomplete without them.

Coral and Amber

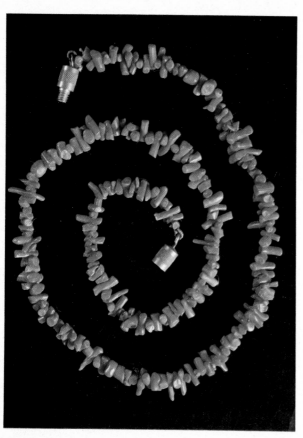

Corals (*right*) are not strictly either rocks or minerals. The corals used for ornaments (*left*) are the skeletons of marine organisms related to jellyfish. These coral organisms build complex skeletons to produce branching or massive structures which form coral reefs. Such reefs are confined to tropical regions. Corals have a long geological history, and their fossils are found in rocks as old as 400 million years. Coral reefs today occur in two main sites: they may form huge barrier reefs, or occur fringing tropical islands.

Amber (*below*) is formed only under special conditions. It is the fossilized resin of extinct fir trees (conifers). Resin is formed on the trunks and branches of conifers, oozing out as a sticky liquid, which rapidly hardens. While it is still sticky, insects get trapped within it. They are then preserved as fossils within the amber, (*previous page*).

Pearl

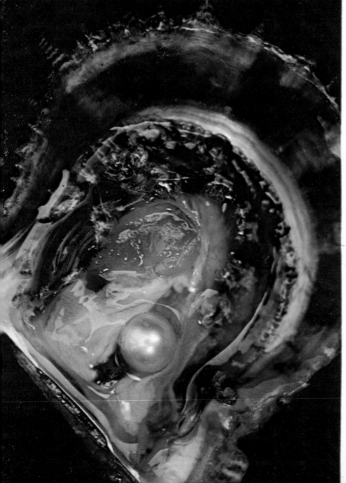

Pearls are formed inside clams, particularly oysters (*bottom left*). They are formed around small objects that get into the living oyster. Pearls are composed of calcium carbonate, like the shells of the oysters themselves. Specks of the right irritant material can be deliberately introduced into oysters to produce cultured pearls. Pearls can also be preserved as fossils – examples as old as 100 million years are known. Unlike gemstones, pearls are readily attacked by acids and other pollutants in the atmosphere. Culture pearls were first obtained by the Chinese in the thirteenth century. The process has been developed into an important industry by the Japanese in the twentieth century; (*top left*) Japanese oyster-beds for the culture of pearls. By the 1960s there were more than 300 sea farms in Japan, and Burma and Australia had also started to establish cultured pearl industries. But natural pearls last much longer and have a much greater value. One of the finest was called 'Star of the West'.

INDEX

Page numbers in italics refer to illustrations

The rock crystal in the cover photograph was provided by the Eaton Bag Co. Ltd., London.

First published in 1979 by
Cathay Books
59 Grosvenor Street, London W1

ISBN 0 86178 003 5

© 1979 Cathay Books

Produced by
Mandarin Publishers Limited
22a Westlands Road
Quarry Bay, Hong Kong

Printed in Singapore.

PDO 79-160